This book belongs to

_____

Every time you read,
To an adult or for pleasure,
Make your way across this map,
Until you reach the treasure!

START →

Conisbrough Castle

Mansion House

Frenchgate Centre

Denaby Main

Doncaster Royal Infirmary

THANK YOU NHS!

Cusworth Hall

Sandall Beat

Doncaster Racecourse

The Dome

Saint George's Minster

Cast theatre

Keepmoat Stadium

Yorkshire Wildlife Park

Danum Shield

Congratulations! You did it!

For Ester, Zoe and Timothy
and the story we're making together

To see and hear the story in English, Czech, Polish or Romanian, use your phone's camera
or a QR code scanner to scan one of the QR codes below...

See and hear the story in English:	Vidíte a slyšíte příběh v češtině:	Zobacz i posłuchaj historii po polsku:	Vedeti si auziti povestea în limba română:

(English)	(Czech)	(Polish)	(Romanian)

With thanks to Ester, Gosia and Ileana.

Doncaster Stories

written and illustrated by Phil Sheppard

BAA CODE BOOKS

you'll find
stories everywhere

Robin Hood Airport

Tales to tell,

to hear, to share.

Be a knight,
    keeping beasts at bay,

Kingdoms to conquer,

dragons to slay.

Solve a crime
like a private eye.

Be a detective,
        a sleuth,
            a spy.

Travel through time,
     have tea with the queen.

Be the greatest hero the world has ever seen.

Feel the thrills
of a death-defying chase.

Overcome obstacles,
win the race.

Go on a quest
    with ghosts from the past.

Battle with warriors,
    fight to the last.

Hear from voices
you'll never know,

Go to places
        you'll never go.

Favourite tales

or tales unknown,

With a tale to tell
you're never alone.

You'll find stories everywhere,

You don't even have to leave your chair.

EVEN IN A DRAGON'S LAIR

BY Ollie, AUCKLEY SCHOOL

Just ask VICtOR the polar bear

by Alfie, Town Field Primary

even in your grandma's hair

by Arianna, St Peter's

Share them with a koala Bear

by Zoe, Town Field Primary

Read with joy and just take care!

Oscar, St Mary's School

on the ground
or in the air

Chgate

by
Addison,
Town
Field
Primary

Even in Your underwear

By Ollie
Southfield Primary

Even in a crowded
fair!

by
Charlotte,
Auckley School

Create your own rhyme and illustration here:

Every time you read,
To an adult or for pleasure,
Make your way across this map,
Until you reach the treasure!

START →

Conisbrough Castle

Mansion House

Frenchgate Centre

Denaby Main

THANK YOU NHS!

Doncaster Royal Infirmary

Cusworth Hall

Sandall Beat

Doncaster Racecourse

Saint George's Minster

Cast theatre

The Dome

Keepmoat Stadium

Yorkshire Wildlife Park

Danum Shield

Congratulations! You did it!

Hi. Phil here, author and illustrator of Doncaster Stories.

As you will have seen, this book features scenes of Doncaster, including lots of little details that help show the history and geography of our town. Did you spot any?

I've made a video that points out a lot of them. It's kind of fun! Take a look by scanning this QR code. You might discover something new! →

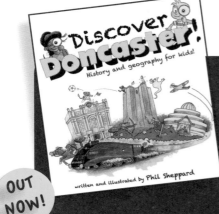

OUT NOW!

Visit my website to find out about my other books, teaching resources and information about author visits, writing workshops & draw-alongs.

www.philshepp.com